Previous works by James S. Adam

The Spirit of Scotland (Ramsay Head Press)
Biblical Ballads and Verses (Claymore Press)
A Fell Fine Baker (Hutchinson Benham Limited)
Contributor to Alistair MacLean Introduces Scotland (Andre Deutsch)
The West Highland Railway (British Rail)
Gaelic Wordbook (W. & R. Chambers Ltd.)
The Business Diaries of Sir Alexander Grant (John Donald Ltd.)
The Declaration of Arbroath: a cassette of this book produced by Scotsoun
New Verses for an Auld Sang (The Herald Press)

To
Marc and Rory
Louise and James
and to the other clans of the
world-wide Family of the Scot

I am so glad that the Declaration has at last been so wonderfully refreshed.
The Earl of Elgin KT.

Thank you very much indeed for letting us have a copy of the 'Declaration of the Scots, 1320'. It is a significant step to have the text of this important statement available in the Latin with translations into English, Scots and Gaelic, and I am very hopeful that this will be used widely in our schools.
The Lord Lyon King of Arms.

'Arbroath' is by far the best you have done yet — sustained and noble.
Sir Alastair Dunnett.

Tha mi fìor thoilichte a' faicinn a leabhar àlainn Obair-bhrothaig. Mile taing air an obair mhòr . . . Can any Scot read these words without pride and emotion, and a renewed sense of the deep roots of our national identity?
Iain MacIver, Keeper of the Manuscripts, National Library.

It is a really splendid production. Getting it printed in Arbroath is a nice touch.
James D. Galbraith, Deputy Keeper, Scottish Record Office.

I felt very privileged to read your presentation, analysis and translations of the Arbroath Declaration. I will treasure it.
Rennie MacOwan, F.S.A. Scot.

Tha sinn fada 'nad chomain airson an leabhair! Nach math a rinn thu! The e glè eireachdail agus samhladh dìleas air an obair a rinn thu. Chaidh obair dhìchiollach am bun na h-obrach seo.
Hugh MacAskill, Gaelic consultant.

Thank you for The Declaration of Arbroath. I was very much impressed by the layout and presentation which is a credit to your publishers. I have always viewed the letter from Arbroath as having a contemporary message for the Scots and I know that your publication will highlight to many people that the sentiments of 1320 still echo today.
Alex Salmond MP

DECLARATION OF THE SCOTS

Letter from Arbroath 1320

EDITED by JAMES S. ADAM

First Printed and Published in 1993
and reprinted in 1995, 1999, 2000 by
The Herald Press Ltd., Arbroath.

Abbey Pageant cover photograph
Credit © STB/Still Moving Picture Company

British Library Cataloguing in Publication Data.

ISBN 0 900454 10 5

Contents:

Preface

By The Rt. Hon. The Earl of Elgin KT

Few historic occasions are better known than the meeting of the Scots Parliament, at Arbroath, which affirmed the despatch of a great Letter to the Pope. The Letter was, of course, written in Latin; but the content must have been considered, talked over, and argued upon in many another language. With these verses James Adam has invoked the passionate feelings of much of contemporary Scotland.

Frankly, I have no idea what tongue my illustrious kinsman customarily used, but he seldom failed to make his verbal message plain. So I have the feeling that he must have had command of at least three languages. Some there be who, perversely, suggest that he could not read: but this, I feel, cannot be true. How else would he have entertained his men waiting impatiently to cross over Loch Lomond? Just as the tale he read on that occasion was of older days and places, knightly deeds and acts of courage, which he possibly translated into Gaelic from the Latin of its original construction, so we have two other poems, each with the richness of affinity to the strength of this great outpouring of a small Nation's pride and dignity.

History's Challenge
to Free Men

The Letter from Arbroath, 1320, is one of the world's great affirmations. It ranks with the handful of historic statements marking the inspiration of men who were caught up in the challenge of their time and of their nation, men who found the shining words that marched with their imperishable ideas.

For the Scot, the Letter from Arbroath to Pope John XXII is especially stirring. The concept of freedom is expressed in a historic Scottish context underlining a people's commitment to be and to remain free.

The Letter was sent as a consequence of the Pope's support for Edward II of England who was decisively beaten at Bannockburn in 1314 but who was persisting in unjustifiable claims over Scotland.

It is a document remarkable for its sturdy independence expressed within a loyalty to the Pope. It is noteworthy also for its Celtic attitude to the power of the Throne.

Almost alone among the nations of feudal Europe where the accepted concept was that authority flowed downward from the crown, Scotland stated clearly and firmly that here the rights flow upward from the people. In the presence of the King, they made it plain that he had their support as long as he did not betray them and that, should he do so, they would choose another King.

The Letter used exceptionally direct language to the Pope and did not hesitate to indicate potential areas of guilt and blame.

There are splendid English translations of the Latin into memorable language of great beauty. I meditated over long years before I acceded to my valued colleague, Alastair Dunnett, who had been prodding me to try a translation in verse form and in Scots. I submit it here, not out of conceit but because I feel that the harder Scots better encompasses the uncompromising sentiments.

I feel that I have achieved acceptable accuracy but I plead one permissible licence. I introduced the phrase "filia specialis ecclesaie", special daughter of the church, a term which had previously been applied to the Scottish Church or, rather, more specifically to the See of Glasgow. Its use here, I think serves to underline the firm reproofs to the Pope expressed in the bluntest of terms.

Well, here is the Letter from Arbroath in a modernised Latin rendering by the Rev. James Quinn SJ, Agnes Mure Mackenzie's translation into stirring English and my rendering into Scots verse — to which as an Angus man I will stand! It seemed to me that the record would be incomplete without a Gaelic version. I have in all humility produced one, after much striving be it said. It was a task away beyond my competence but someone had to bell that cat which keeps popping up throughout our history.

Over the years, I have tried on my own to arrive at some understanding of Gaelic and I am grateful to my recent tutors, Ronald Black of the Department of Celtic, Edinburgh University, and Morag MacLeod of the School of Scottish Studies. I am grateful also for the encouragement of Chrissie McAuslane and Hugh MacAskill, both originally from Skye. My particular thanks to Hugh who painstakingly guided me through a long correspondence and helped greatly in directing me into making my Gaelic follow more closely my intentions, to Canon MacNeill of Fort William, native of Barra, Gaelic scholar and bard, who freely gave his welcome advice and to my friends at that time all involved in Comunn na Gaidhlig, John A. MacKay, Donald John MacLeod and Katie MacGregor for the final revision of my Gaelic version. In the Summer 1991 issue of Gairm, the prestigious Gaelic quarterly, Professor Derick Thomson published the Gaelic version. Needless to say, I am grateful to have his accolade and his sub-editing! If any imperfections remain to offend the Gaelic purist, the responsibility is solely mine — gabh mo leisgeul.

Father James Quinn SJ has patiently coped with the demands I made on his time and knowledge. My grateful thanks to him.

I value greatly the informed preface from The Earl of Elgin, head of the world-wide Bruce family of which King Robert Bruce was so distinguished a member. It is a family which has contributed much, and in many fields, throughout half our recorded history and which maintains today that honoured tradition.

I am delighted also to be able to include a postscript from Andy Stewart, native of Glasgow with close family connections in Arbroath, who was made the first Freeman of the District of Angus in June, 1987, internationally namely as an entertainer, singer and writer of songs which ring in the ears of Scots across the world. Unhappily, as the last pre-publication details were being finalised, we heard the sad news of Andy's death. His own Postscript makes a fitting memorial and is a moving personal statement of how he saw his country, his people, and their history.

My many friends have understood what it was that I was trying to achieve. I had as my objective the production of an acceptable brochure for general reader interest which might also have a role in the schools. Letter from Arbroath is a major Caledonian statement in which we can all take pride. So here it is in stirring English, implacable Scots and I trust, acceptable Gaelic, and also in a modernised Latin. Scrieve fae Aberbrothock appeared in the 1986 Winter Issue of Scottish Ambassador. The Parchment of the original letter is reproduced by permission of the Keeper of the Records of Scotland with the agreement of the Controller of HM Stationery Office. The Trustees for Agnes Mure Mackenzie kindly gave permission for the use of her translation.

Incidentally, all Scots have reason to thank the late Tom Johnston who used his authority as Secretary of State for Scotland to instruct the Stationery Office to print and make the Declaration of Arbroath available at a price within the reach of our schools and citizens. The Stationery Office has now discontinued the publication but copies can be obtained from the Scottish Record Office.

J.S.A.

Letter from Arbroath

A translation by Agnes Mure Mackenzie

To our Lord and Very Holy Father in Christ, Lord John, the Supreme Pontiff, by God's Providence, of the Most Holy Roman and Catholic Church, his humble and devoted sons — Duncan, Earl of Fife; Thomas Randolph, Earl of Moray, Lord of Man and of Annandale; Patrick Dunbar, Earl of March; Malise, Earl of Strathearn; Malcolm, Earl of Lennox; William, Earl of Ross; Magnus, Earl of Caithness and Orkney; and William, Earl of Sutherland; Walter, Stewart of Scotland; William Soules, Butler of Scotland; James, Lord of Douglas; Roger Mowbray; David, Lord of Brechin; David Graham; Ingram Umfraville; John Menteith, guardian of the earldom of Menteith; Alexander Fraser; Gilbert Hay, Constable of Scotland; Robert Keith, Marischal of Scotland; Henry St. Clair; John Graham; David Lindsay; William Oliphant; Patrick Graham; John Fenton; William Abernethy; David Wemyss; William Mushet; Fergus of Ardrossan; Eustace Maxwell; William Ramsay; William Mowat; Alan Murray; Donald Campbell; John Cameron; Reginald Cheyne; Alexander Seton; Andrew Leslie; and Alexander Straiton — and other barons and freeholders, with the whole Commons of the Kingdom of Scotland. With all filial reverence devoutly do we kiss your blessed feet.

From the deeds alike and the books of our forefathers, we understand, Most Holy Lord and Father, that among other noble nations our own, the Scottish, grows famous for many men of wide renown. The which Scottish nation, journeying from Greater Scythia by the Tyrrhene Sea and the Pillars of Hercules, could not in any place or time or manner be overcome by the barbarians, though long dwelling in Spain among the fiercest of them. Coming thence, twelve hundred years after the transit of Israel, with many victories and many toils they won that habitation in the West, which though the Britons have been driven out, the Picts effaced, and the Norwegians, Danes and English have often assailed it, they hold now, in freedom from all vassalage; and as the old historians bear witness, have ever so held it. In this kingdom have reigned a hundred and thirteen kings of their own Blood

Royal, and no man foreign has been among them. Of their merits and their noble qualities we need say no more, for they are bright enough by this alone, that though they were placed in the furthest ends of the earth, Our Lord Jesus Christ, Who is the King of Kings, called them among the first to His most firm faith, after His Passion and Resurrection. Nor did He choose to confirm them in the Lord's Faith by any one less than His own first Apostle (although he stands second or third in order of rank) the most gracious Andrew, brother of Peter's self, whom ever since He has established their Patron.

Bearing all these things carefully in mind, those holiest of fathers, your predecessors, adorned and fortified this kingdom and people, as belonging especially to Peter's brother, with many favours and many privileges. Thus our nation till now has lived under their protection in peace and quiet, till the Magnificent Prince, Edward King of the English, the father of the Edward that now is, did, under cover of alliance and friendship, invade and occupy as an enemy our kingdom and people, who then had no head, who had in mind no evil towards him, and who then were unused to war or sudden invasion. What that king has done in wrongs and slaughter and violence, in imprisonings of the leaders of the Church, in burning and looting of religious houses and the massacres of their communities, with his other outrages on the Scottish people (sparing nor sex nor age nor priestly orders) is something that is not to be comprehended save by those who know these things from their own experience.

Yet, at last, by His help Who heals and sains the wounded, we are freed from these innumerable evils by our most valiant Sovereign, King, and Lord, King Robert, who to set free his heritage and his people faced, like a new Maccabeus or Joshua, with joyful heart, toil, weariness, hardship, and dangers. By the Providence of God, the right of succession, those laws and customs which we are resolved to defend even with our lives, and by our own just consent, he is our King: and to him who has brought salvation to his people through the safeguarding of our liberties, as much by his own deserving as by his own rights, we hold and choose in all things to adhere. Yet Robert himself, should he turn aside from the task that he has begun, and yield Scotland or us to the English King and people, we should cast out as the enemy of us all, as subverter of our rights and of his own, and should choose another king to defend our freedom: for so long as a hundred of us are left alive, we will yield in no least way to English dominion. We fight not for glory nor for wealth nor honours; but only and alone we fight for freedom, which no good man surrenders but with his life.

Because of these things, most reverend Father and Lord, praying earnestly from our hearts that before Him as Whose Vicar on Earth you reign, before Him to Whom there is but a single weight, Who has but one law for Jew and Greek and for Scots and English — before Him will with honesty consider the manifest anguish and tribulation which we and the Church have suffered through the English, and will look upon us with a father's eyes. We pray you to admonish this King of England (to whom his own possessions may well suffice, since England of old was enough for seven kings or more) that he should leave us in peace in our little Scotland, since we desire no more than is our own, and have no dwelling place beyond our own borders: and we on our part, for the sake of peace, are willing to do all within our power.

Most Holy Father, it is your part to do this, or surrender to the barbarity of the heathen, let loose for the sins of Christians on the Faithful, and daily forcing the bounds of Christendom, and you know it would mar the security of your fame if you looked unmoved on anything which in your time should bring dishonour on any part of the Church. May your Holiness therefore admonish those Christian princes who falsely claim that their own wars with their neighbours now hinder them from relieving the Holy Land: though indeed they are hindered only by their belief that they will find more profit and less toil in crushing neighbours smaller than themselves, who appear to them also weaker than themselves. He Who knows all knows that if the King of the English would leave us in peace, we and our own Lord King would go joyfully thither: which thing we solemnly testify and declare to the Vicar of Christ and to all Christian people. But if too readily, or insincerely, you put your faith in what the English have told you, and continue to favour them, to our confounding, then indeed shall the slaying of bodies, yea and of souls, and all those evils which they shall do to us, or we to them, be charged to your account by the Most High.

We are always bound to you, as God's Viceregent, to please you by a son's obedience in all things. We remit our cause to the Highest King and Judge, casting our care on Him, in the hope and faith that He will grant to us both strength and valour, and bring about our enemies' overthrow.

May the Most High preserve for many years Your Serene Highness to His Holy Church.

Given at the Monastery of Arbroath in Scotland the sixth day of April in the year of Grace one thousand three hundred and twenty, and in the fifteenth year of the King named above.

Scrieve fae Aberbrothock
til Pap John the twenty-saicont,
1320

Maist Haly Faither in our Lord
an Sovereign Pontiff maist respectit,
bi God's great Provenance an will
owre universal Kirk electit;
our heichest gentles gaithert here,
wi barons, free men, aa assemblit,
speak strang for Scotland's truest saul,
for Kinrik hale an undividit.

Lang years hae we been privileged sons
in Kirk o filia specialis,
a mark we wear wi humill pride
in Him whase covenant that seal is;
we here subscrieve oursels the bairns
o dochter waled for special portion,
obedient sons wha firmly pledge
your taes tae kiss in deep devotion.

Twas kent, O Haly Faither Lord,
langsyne, mang aa the noble nations,
fae Galilee, Galatia, Gaul,
Galicia fiercest o barbarians,
that we had men o great renown
wha aye held stark tae freedom's schulin,
nor man, nor nation e'er daured claim
dominion owre our people rulin.

Three thousan years our faithers toiled
an focht tae win this habitation
'gainst Briton, Pict, Norwegian, Dane,
but maist against the Inglis nation;
nou we staun free this day an aye
as witnessed by ilk auld historian,
a hundert Kings an thirteen ruled
o our ain bluid an nae man alien.

The Scots wha dwalt at warld's faur edge,
amang the first o Christ's clear callin,
the King o Kings twas gied the grace
o Anndra Sanct tae gaird their fallin,
the Lord's ain first Apostle true,
the Rock Sanct Peter's ain dear brither,
wha aye sin then has been tae us
the Patron tae whase hairt we gaither.

An sae this Kinrik an its fowk,
adorned bi aa the Haly Faithers,
grew strang as Peter's brither's bairns
wi mony privileges an favours;
we dwalt in peace neath Anndra's airms
til Edward under freenly guises
set out tae yoke on us in war
an ruthless, sudden, fierce invade us.

There's nane can comprehend the wrangs,
the slauchter sad, the evil violence,
save they wha suffered at his hauns
the massacres that wrocht daith's silence,
the kirks, the abbeys, aa destroyed,
gien owre tae Saxon brutish murders,
nor sparin sex, nor auld, nor young,
we nae respect for priestly orders.

Our Prince an hero Robert fiere
focht lang like Judas Maccabeus
tae shaw aince mair gainst Southron guile
nae tyrant yet is born tae rule us;
thru sair-bocht years, he kept guid hairt
an tholit dang'rous ploys an hairdship
tae ward his people wha had stuid
wi him tae haud their nation's heirship.

The Declaration of Arbroath 1320

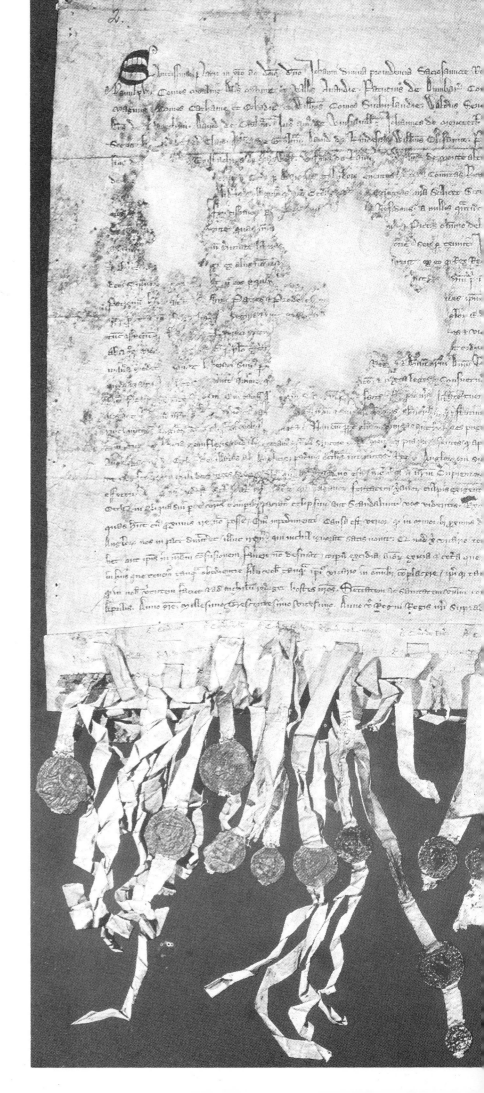

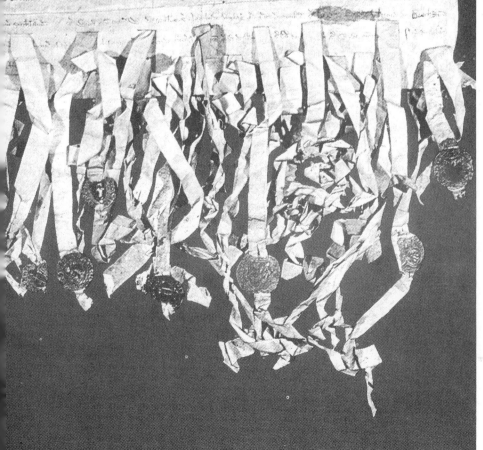

Bi our consent he sits as King,
a safeguard strang o Scotland's freedom,
bi his ain richt an his ain warth;
for baith, we'll fecht wi micht an smeddum:
yet sud he e'er hae cheenge o mind
an sweir a bann tae sairve the Inglis,
we'll haud him nane the mair our King
an wale a wycer man tae lead us.

We hae nae need tae pruive anew
the honour sung in Scotland's story,
we pit nae trust in treach'rous pelf,
nor dae we seek the fause vainglory,
but ilk ane here will aye bide free
tho we be left alane a hundert —
be shair, that life itsel we'll gie,
mang slaves, we never sall be numbert.

There's but ae law for Jew an Greek
an ane alane for Scot an Saxon,
for He abune will judge the wrangs
owre anguished years o tribulation;
O Lord, we plead ye, curb the greed
that Ingland's King aye flaunts about him
wha sud hae mair nor aa his need
whaur seiven kings aince shared his kingdom.

We seek but that whilk is our ain
within this little kintra dwellin,
sae gar him leave us here tae bide;
tae pledge our peace, we're mair than willin:
Maist Haly Faither tell him straucht,
your duty's clear, ye downa jouk it,
or heathen host will see in sin
the Kirk in deep dishonour bookit.

Rebuke thae kings wha sleekit claim
that only wars wi neebours hinder
the Haly Land's relief, their aim,
while thrang they weaker nations plunder;
the God wha reads aa hairts kens this
— wi Edward aff our backs removit —
we'd joy the Haly Land tae free,
an tryst wi ye an Kirk tae pruive it.

The Declaration of Arbroath (English Translation)

To the most Holy Father and Lord in Christ, the Lord John, by divine providence Supreme Pontiff of the Holy Roman and Universal Church, his humble and devout sons Duncan, Earl of Fife, Thomas Randolph, Earl of Moray, Lord of Man and of Annandale, Patrick Dunbar, Earl of March, Malise, Earl of Strathearn, Malcolm, Earl of Lennox, William, Earl of Ross, Magnus, Earl of Caithness and Orkney, and William, Earl of Sutherland; Walter, Steward of Scotland, William Soules, Butler of Scotland, James, Lord of Douglas, Roger Mowbray, David, Lord of Brechin, David Graham, Ingram Umfraville, John Menteith, guardian of the earldom of Menteith, Alexander Fraser, Gilbert Hay, Constable of Scotland, Robert Keith, Marischal of Scotland, Henry St Clair, John Graham, David Lindsay, William Oliphant, Patrick Graham, John Fenton, William Abernethy, David Wemyss, William Mushet, Fergus of Ardrossan, Eustace Maxwell, William Ramsay, William Mowat, Alan Murray, Donald Campbell, John Cameron, Reginald Cheyne, Alexander Seton, Andrew Leslie, and Alexander Straiton, and the other barons and freeholders and the whole community of the realm of Scotland send all manner of filial reverence, with devout kisses of his blessed feet.

Most Holy Father and Lord, we know and from the chronicles and books of the ancients we find that among other famous nations our own, the Scots, has been graced with widespread renown. They journeyed from Greater Scythia by way of the Tyrrhenian Sea and the Pillars of Hercules, and dwelt for a long course of time in Spain among the most savage tribes, but nowhere could they be subdued by any race, however barbarous. Thence they came, twelve hundred years after the people of Israel crossed the Red Sea, to their home in the west where they still live today. The Britons they first drove out, the Picts they utterly destroyed, and, even though very often assailed by the Norwegians, the Danes and the English, they took possession of that home with many victories and untold efforts; and, as the historians of old time bear witness, they have held it free of all bondage ever since. In their kingdom there have reigned one hundred and thirteen kings of their own royal stock, the line unbroken a single foreigner.

The high qualities and deserts of these people, were they not otherwise manifest, gain glory enough from this: that the King of kings and Lord of lords, our Lord Jesus Christ, after His Passion and Resurrection, called them, even though settled in the uttermost parts of the earth, almost the first to His most holy faith. Nor would He have them confirmed in that faith by merely anyone but by the first of His Apostles -- by calling, though second or third in rank -- the most gentle Saint Andrew, the Blessed Peter's brother, and desired him to keep them under his protection as their patron forever.

The Most Holy Fathers your predecessors gave careful heed to these things and bestowed many favours and numerous privileges on this same kingdom and people, as being the special charge of the Blessed Peter's brother. Thus our nation under their protection did indeed live in freedom and peace up to the time when that mighty prince the King of the English, Edward, the father of the one who reigns today, when our kingdom had no head and our people harboured no malice or treachery and were then unused to wars or invasions, came in the guise of a friend and ally to harass them as an enemy. The deeds of cruelty, massacre, violence, pillage, arson, imprisoning prelates, burning down monasteries, robbing and killing monks and nuns, and yet other outrages without number which he committed against our people, sparing neither age nor sex, religion nor rank, no one could describe nor fully imagine unless he had seen them with his own eyes.

But from these countless evils we have been set free, by the help of Him Who though He afflicts yet heals and restores, by our most tireless Prince, King and Lord, the Lord Robert. He, that his people and his heritage might be delivered out of the hands of our enemies, met toil and fatigue, hunger and peril, like another Macabaeus or Joshua and bore them cheerfully. Him, too, divine providence, his right of

succession according to or laws and customs which we shall maintain to the death, and the due consent and assent of us all have made our Prince and King. To him, as to the man by whom salvation has been wrought unto our people, we are bound both by law and by his merits that our freedom may be still maintained, and by him, come what may, we mean to stand.

Yet if he should give up what he has begun, and agree to make us or our kingdom subject to the King of England or the English, we should exert ourselves at once to drive him out as our enemy and a subverter of his own rights and ours, and make some other man who was well able to defend us our King; for, as long as but a hundred of us remain alive, never will we on any conditions be brought under English rule. It is in truth not for glory, nor riches, nor honours that we are fighting, but for freedom -- for that alone, which no honest man gives up but with life itself.

Therefore it is, Reverend Father and Lord, that we beseech your Holiness with our most earnest prayers and suppliant hearts, inasmuch as you will in your sincerity and goodness consider all this, that, since with Him Whose Vice-Regent on earth you are there is neither weighing nor distinction of Jew and Greek, Scotsman or Englishman, you will look with the eyes of a father on the troubles and privation brought by the English upon us and upon the Church of God. May it please you to admonish and exhort the King of the English, who ought to be satisfied with what belongs to him since England used once to be enough for seven kings or more, to leave us Scots in peace, who live in this poor little Scotland, beyond which there is no dwelling-place at all, and covet nothing but our own. We are sincerely willing to do anything for him, having regard to our condition, that we can, to win peace for ourselves.

This truly concerns you, Holy Father, since you see the savagery of the heathen raging against the Christians, as the sins of Christians have indeed deserved, and the frontiers of Christendom being pressed inward every day; and how much it will tarnish your Holiness's memory if (which God forbid) the Church suffers eclipse or scandal in any branch of it during your time, you must perceive. Then rouse the Christian princes who for false reasons pretend that they cannot go to help of the Holy Land because of wars they have on hand with their neighbours. The real reason that prevents them is that in making war on their smaller neighbours they find quicker profit and weaker resistance. But how cheerfully our Lord the King and we too would go there if the King of the English would leave us in peace, He from Whom nothing is hidden well knows; and we profess and declare it to you as the Vicar of Christ and to all Christendom.

But if your Holiness puts too much faith in the tales the English tell and will not give sincere belief to all this, nor refrain from favouring them to our prejudice, then the slaughter of bodies, the perdition of souls, and all the other misfortunes that will follow, inflicted by them on us and by us on them, will, we believe, be surely laid by the Most High to your charge.

To conclude, we are and shall ever be, as far as duty calls us, ready to do your will in all things, as obedient sons to you as His Vicar; and to Him as the Supreme King and Judge we commit the maintenance of our cause, csating our cares upon Him and firmly trusting that He will inspire us with courage and bring our enemies to nought.

May the Most High preserve you to his Holy Church in holiness and health and grant you length of days.

Given at the monastery of Arbroath in Scotland on the sixth day of the month of April in the year of grace thirteen hundred and twenty and the fifteenth year of the reign of our King aforesaid.

lorsed: Letter directed to our Lord the Supreme Pontiff by the community of Scotland.

litional names written on some of the seal tags: Alexander Lamberton, Edward Keith, John Inchmartin, Thomas nzies, John Durrant, Thomas Morham (and one illegible).

Obedient sons we aye are bound,
Maist Sovereign Hie, tae please Ye,
yet here we staun afore our God
an counsel clear we plain maun rede Ye:
ye canna tak an Inglis word
an gie't alane your simple trustin,
nor may Ye yet in dark deceit
ding doun on us war's reid encrustin.

The evil deeds they'll wreak on us,
or evils waur we'll quick return them,
thae awesome debts, tae your account
the Lord Maist Hie will grim record them;
if blinnd Ye swim wi Inglis tide,
Ye'll doom us aa tae shair destruction,
the Deil's ain slauchters, corp an saul,
Ye'll answer at the Resurrection.

Sae tae the Throne our cause we bring
afore the Michty King wha gied us
the mind oppressions woes tae fecht
in God's great name an Christ's wha freed us,
in howp an faith that He will grant
tae us the courage strang an bydand,
that we may haud our nation free
an cowp for aye usurpin tyrant.

An be Ye spared the Kirk tae sairve,
this 1320th year sae blessit;
gien at Arbroath on Aprile Saxt,
in fifteenth year o King aforesaid.

Litir o Obair-bhrothaig gu Pap Ian XXII, 1320

O Athair ro naomh an seirbhis Dhè
's ceannard mòr ro urramaicht',
le toil is cumhachd mhòrachd Dhè
os cionn na h-Eaglais iomlan taght';
ar daoine uaisle saor le chèile,
ceann cinnidh àrdaicht' againn cruinnicht',
thaobh anam Alba bruidhinn treun
airson rìoghachd gu lèir is aonaicht'.

Mar mhic gu sochair tro' linntean fad'
an Eaglais *filia specialis,*
le pròis is irioslachd san Tì a chuir
sar chomharra chùmhnant naomha oirnn;
mar leanabh nighean àraidh roghnaicht',
seo sgrìobh sinn fhèin an ùmhlachd trom
bhur mic gu bràth, an gealladh làidir
an cràbhadh fìor bhur casan 'pògadh.

Bhathas 'tuigse, Thighearn Athair Naomh,
tro' uine fad' measg muinntir mhòr
bho Ghalile, Galatia, Gaul,
Galicia nas gairge nan slògh borb',
gum bi ar laochan cliùiteach fìor
air saorsa grèim gu daingeann cumail;
an togradh duibh cuir sinn fo riaghal —
nach dànaich duin' no dùthaich eil'.

Fad mìltean bliadhna cruaidhe trom
an aghaidh Bhreatannach, Lochlann's eile,
ar n-athraichean air strì ar tìr a chumail
an saors' bho Shasainn sanntach glacail;
a-nis am fianais le eachdair' sean,
an-diugh nar seasamh nar fir sìorraidh,
bha againn ceud is trì rìghrean deug
gun coigrich breugach air ar rìoghachd.

An àitibh iomallach a' chruinne-cè
a-measg nam poball an toiseach a dh'èisd
gairm soilleir Chrìosda, ga chreidsinn,
fhuair gràs o Rìgh nan Rìghrean,
's Anndra Naomh an ceuman dluth a' cumail,
'na bhràthair fìor do Phàdraig Carraig,
on àm sin is e a tha gar dìon,
sar Abstol gus Alba a ghlèidheadh.

Tro' linntean dh'fhàs ar rìoghachd 's ar daoine
beannaicht' len athraiche naomha gu lèir
mar chlann gu sònraicht' bhràthair Phàdraig
le mòran càirdeis, bàidhealachd is sochair,
fo dhìon Anndra an sìth a' còmhnaidh —
gus Eideard ann an càirdeas breugach
gu grad rinn cogadh garg nar n-aghaidh
's fear cruaidh gar cur fo èiginn brònach.

Chan urrain dhaibh na h-uilc a thuigsinn
nach fhaca marbhadh agus ainneart
ach iadsan dh'fhuiling on Rìgh neo-airidh
am mulad dubh, am bàs cho tosdach,
na h-eaglaisean, abaidean uile, air sgrios
am marbhadh brùideil borb gun chiall,
nach seachainn bodach, bean no leanabh,
gun urram air na sagairtean bàidheil.

Rinn Raibeart treun ar Prionnsa gaisgeil
stri mhòr mar Iudas Maccabeus,
a chur ar cùl bruadaran Shasainn
le aintighearn a chaoidh nar riaghladh;
tro' bhliadhna trom, chridh' treun a' cumail
gu maireann, fad cruaidh chunnart' mòr
a' dìon le sgiath nas cinntich fìor
a mhuinntir sheas air taobh na h-oighreachd.

Chuir sinn air àirde Rìgh nar taghadh,
fear glèidhidh treun air saorsa Alba,
a rugadh 'na rìgh is 'na dhuine fiùthail,
airson sin tha sinne deas ri sabaid.
Ma strìochdas e anfhann gar trèigsinn,
sin bitheamaid grad 'n Righ ud a dhiùltadh,
ma ghèilleas e fhèin ri seirbhis Shasainn,
'n sin Rìgh nas fheàrr bidh sinn a' taghadh.

Chan fheum sinn dearbhadh a-rithist
an glòirbhinn mhòr an sgeulachd Alba,
cha chuir sinn earbs' an airgead mealltach,
chan iarr sinn ràiteachas gun fhiù,
cha bhi sinn gu dìlinn a' gèilleadh
fo thràillealachd ìsle Shasainn amh,
cho fad's a mhaireas ceud a-mhàin
glèidhidh sinn gu treun ar saors' gu bràth.

Aon lagh air Iùdhach is Greugach a-mhàin
mar sin an Alba 's Sasann cuideachd,
bidh an Tì as àirde toirt a bhreitheanais
air uilc fad bliadhn' dorcha dòrainneach.
A Thighearn, tha sinn ag achanaich, cuir stad
air sannt Rìgh ud na h-uile Sasuinn
a tha leis an talamh nas mò 'na fheum
far an d'fhuair seachd Rìghrean sàsachd.

Is sinne an còmhnaidh nar dùthaich bhig,
chan iarr sinn ach rudan is leinn fhèin,
sin innis dha leig dhuinn bhith ciùin,
ar sìth a ghealladh tha sinn deònach.
Chan urrain dhuibh gu dearbh seachnadh
bhur dleasnas soilleir, Athair as naomha,
mus fhaic am pàganach peacach Eaglais
's a h-ainm dol sìos am masladh grànda.

Sin cronaich Rìghrean an leisgeil bhreugaich
nach urrain dhaibh Tir Naomh a' chuideach,
a chionn a' chogaidh an aghaidh nàbaidh,
's iad trang aig creachadh an coimhnearsnach;
is aithne do Dhia a leugh an cridhe —
gun eallach Eideard, bhitheamaid deas
le aoibhneas saorsa thoirt don Tìr,
's an làthair Eaglais bheir sinn gealladh.

Nis deanamaid ùmhlachd dhuibh mar mhic
is a bhith taitneach daonnan d'ur toil,
ach seasamh an seo am fianais ar Dia
is feumaidh sinn ar comhairle fhoillseach —
na gabh gun dearbhadh facal Shasainn,
na cuir ann bhur muinighin neochiontach,
neo-chùramach na dèan ar tilgeadh
an cogadh dòrainneach brònach fuileach.

Gach olc a chuireadh iadsan oirnne,
am mulad ceudna 's e an dìoghladh leinne,
a Dhè as Àirde, na cionta sin
cho uabharr, dona, fo chùnntas cuir-sa;
bithidh sgrios gu lèir air àitibh uile,
ma chumas sibhse bhur taic ri Sasainn
an casgradh diabhlaidh air corp is anam
aig aiseirigh feumaidh sibh am freagradh.

Do chathair Dhè bheir sinn ar cùis
air beulaibh an Rìgh ro Mhòr ar breitheamh;
ar n-inntinn uaith ri fòirneart a' cathadh
an ainm Dhè is earbsa Chrìosd,
gu robh ar Dia a' deònach dhuinn
a' mhisneach làidir treun is seasmhach,
gun cumadh sinn ar cinneach saor
's gu'n còpadh sinn aintighearnas daingeann.

Gu maireadh sibh an seirbhis Eaglais
a' bhliadhna 1320 beannaicht';
bho Obair-bhrothaig Giblean sèathamh
an còigeamh bliadhn' deug an Rìgh roimh-ainmicht'.

From the Latin of the parchment in the Scottish Record Office, Edinburgh

Sanctissimo Patri in Christo ac domino, domino Johanni divina providencia Sacrosauncte Romane et Universalis Ecclesie Summo Pontifici, Filii Sui Humiles et devoti, Duncanus Comes de Fyf, Thomas Ranulphi Comes Moravie Dominus Mannie et Vallis Anandie, Patricius de Dumbar Comes Marchie, Malisius Comes de Stratheryne, Malcolmus Comes de Levenax, Willelmus Comes de Ross, Magnus Comes Cathanie et Orkadie et Willelmus Comes Suthirlandie, Walterus Senescallus Scocie, Willelmus de Soules Buttelarius Scocie, Jacobus Dominus de Duglas, Rogerus de Moubray, David Dominus de Brechyn, David de Graham, Ingeramus de Umfravill, Johannes de Meneteth Custos Comitatus de Meneteth, Alexander Fraser, Gilbertus de Haya Constabularius Scocie, Robertus de Keth Marescallus Scocie, Henricus de Sancto Claro, Johannes de Graham, David de Lindesay, Willelmus Olifaunt, Patricius de Graham, Johannes de Fenton, Willelmus de Abirnithy, David de Wemys, Willelmus de Montefixo, Fergusius de Ardrossane, Eustachius de Maxwell, Willelmus de Ramesay, Willelmus de Montealto, Alanus de Moravia, Douenaldus Cambell, Johannes Cambrun, Reginaldus le chen, Alexander de Setoun, Andreas de Lescelyne et Alexander de Stratoun Ceterique Barones et Liberetenentes ac tota Communitas Regni Scocie, omnimodam Reverenciam filialem cum devotis Pedum osculis beatorum. Scimus Sanctissime Pater et Domine, et ex antiquorum gestis et libris Colligimus, quod inter Ceteras naciones egregias, nostra Scilicet Scottorum Nacio multis preconiis fuerit insignita que de Majori Schithia per Mare tirenum et Columpnas Herculis transiens, et in Hispania inter ferocissimos, per multa temporum curricula Residens: a nullis quantumcunque barbaricis poterat allicubi subiugari, Indeque veniens post mille et ducentos annos a transitu populi israelitici, sibi sedes in Occidente quas nunc optinet, expulsis Britonibus et Pictis omnino deletis, licet per Norwagienses, Dacos et Anglicos sepius impugnata fuerit, multis sibi victoriis et laboribus quamplurimis adquisiuit, ipsasque ab omni servitute liberas, ut Priscorum testantur Historie, semper tenuit. In quorum Regno Centum et Tresdecim Reges de ipsorum Regali prosapia nullo alienigena interveniente, Regnaverunt. Quorum Nobilitates et merita, licet ex aliis non clarerent, satis patenter effulgent, ex eo quod Rex Regum et dominus Jhesus Christos post passionem et Resurreccionem suam, ipsos in ultimis terre finibus constitutos, quasi primus ad suam fidem sanctissimam convocavit nec eos per quemlibet in dicta fide confirmari voluit, set per suum primum apostolum quamuis ordine secundum vel tercium scilicet Andream mitissimum beati Petri Germanum quem semper ipsis preesse voluit ut Patronum. Hec autem Sanctissimi Patres et Predecessores vestri sollicita mente pensantes, ipsum Regnum et populum ut beati Petri germani peculium, multis favoribus et privilegiis quamplurimis munierunt. Ita quod gens nostra sub ipsorum proteccione libera, hactenus deguit et quieta, donec ille Princeps Magnificus Rex Anglorum Edwardus pater istius qui nunc est, Regnum nostrum acephalum populumque nullius mali, aut doli conscium, nec bellis, aut insultibus tunc assuetum, sub amici et confederati specie inimicabiliter infestavit, Cuius iniurias, Cedes et violencias, predaciones, incendia, prelatorum incarceraciones, monasteriorum combustiones, Religiosorum spoliaciones, et occisiones alia quoque enormia, que in dicto populo excercuit nulli parcens etati, aut sexui, Religioni aut ordini, nullus scriberet, nec ad plenum intelligeret, nisi quem experiencia informaret. A quibus malis innumeris ipso Juvante, qui post vulnera medetur et sanat liberati sumus per strenuissimum Principem Regem et Dominum nostrum Dominum Robertum, qui pro populo et hereditate suis de manibus Inimicorum liberandis quasi alter Machabeus aut Josue, labores et tedia inedias et pericula, leto sustinuit animo; quem eciam divina disposicio, et iuxta leges et Consuetudines nostras, quas usque ad mortem sustinere volumus Juris successio, et debitus nostrorum omnium Consensus et Assensus nostrum fecerunt Principem atque Regem, Cui tanquam illi per quem salus in populo facta est, pro nostra libertate tuenda, tam Jure quam meritis, tenemur et volumus in omnibus adherere. Quem si ab inceptis desisteret, Regi Anglorum, aut Anglicis nos aut Regnum nostrum volens subicere, tanquam Inimicum nostrum et sui, nostrique Juris subversorem, statim expellere niteremur, et alium Regem nostrum, qui ad defensionem nostram sufficeret, faceremus. Quia quamdiu Centum vivi remanserint, nuncquam Anglorum dominio aliquatenus volumus subiugari, Non enim propter gloriam, divicias aut honores pugnamus, set propter libertatem solummodo, quam Nemo bonus, nisi simul cum vita amittit. Hinc est Reverende Pater et Domine quod sanctitatem vestram omni precum instancia genuflexis cordibus exoramus, quatenus sincero corde, menteque pia recensentes, quod apud eum, cuius vices in terris geritis, non sit Pondus et pondus, nec distinccio Judei et greci, Scoti aut Anglici, tribulaciones et angustias nobis et Ecclesie dei illatas ab Anglicis, paternis oculis intuentes, Regem Anglorum cui sufficere debet quod possidet, cum olim Anglia septem aut pluribus solebat sufficere Regibus, monere et exhortari dignemini ut nos Scotos in exili degentes Scocia ultra quam habitacio non est, nichilque nisi nostrum Cupientes in pace dimittat, Cui pro nostra procuranda quiete, quicquid possumus ad statum nostrum Respectu habito, facere volumus cum effectu. Vestra enim interest Sancte Pater hoc facere, qui paganorum feritatem, Christianorum culpis exigentibus in Christianos sevientem aspicitis, et Christianorum terminos artari in dies, (quantumque vestre) sanctitatis memorie derogat si quod absit Ecclesia in aliqua sui parte vestris temporibus patiatur eclipsim, aut Scandalum, vos videritis. Excitet igitur Christianos Principes qui non causam ut causam ponentes se fingunt in subsidium terre sancte propter guerras quas habent, cum proximis ire non posse, Cuius impedimenti, Causa est verior, quod in minoribus proximis debellandis, utilitas propior et resistencia debilior estimantur. Set quam leto corde dictus dominus Rex noster et Nos si Rex Anglorum nos in pace dimitteret, illuc iremus, qui nichil ignorat satis novit. Quod Christi vicario, totique Christianitati, ostendimus et testamur, quibus si sanctitas vestra Anglorum relatibus nimis credula fidem sinceram non adhibet, aut ipsis in nostram confusionem favere non desinat, corporum excidia, animarum exicia et cetera que sequentur incommoda, que ipsi in nobis et Nos in ipsis fecerimus, vobis ab altissimo credimus imputanda, ex quo sumus et erimus in hiis que tenemur tanquam obediencie filii vobis tanquam ipsius vicario in omnibus complacere, ipsique tanquam Summo Regi et Judici, causam nostram tuendam committimus, Cogitatum nostram Jactantes, in ipso sperantesque firmiter quod in nobis virtutem faciet et ad nichilum rediget hostes nostros. Sanctitatem ac sanitatem vestram conservet Altissimus Ecclesie sue sancte per tempora diuturna. Datum apud Monasterium Abirbrothoc, in Scocia, sexto die Aprilis, Anno gracie, Millesimo Trescentesimo vicesimo Anno vero Regni Regis nostri supradicti, Quinto decimo.

Exemplar litterarum ad Joannem Papam XXII missarum, Aberbrothocii in Scotia anno MCCCXX datarum.

Sanctissimo Patri in Christo ac Domino, Domino Joanni divina providentia sacrosanctae Romanae et universalis Ecclesiae Summo Pontifici, filii sui humiles et devoti:

Duncanus, comes de Fife, Thomas Ranulphi, comes Moraviae, dominus Manniae et Vallis Annandiae, Patricius de Dunbar, comes Marchiae, Malisius, comes de Strathearn, Malcolmus, comes de Lennox, Willelmus, comes de Ross, Magnus, comes Cathaniae et Orcadiae, et Willelmus, comes Sutherlandiae, Walterus, seneschallus Scotiae, Willelmus de Soules, buttelarius Scotiae, Jacobus, dominus de Douglas, Rogerus de Mowbray, David, dominus de Brechin, David de Graham, Ingramus de Umfraville, Joannes de Menteith, custos comitatus de Menteith, Alexander Fraser, Gilbertus de Haya, constabularius Scotiae, Robertus de Keith, mareschallus Scotiae, Henricus de Sancto Claro, Joannes de Graham, David de Lindsay, Willelmus Oliphant, Patricius de Graham, Joannes de Fenton, Willelmus de Abernethy, David de Wemyss, Willelmus de Montefixo, Fergusius de Ardrossan, Eustachius de Maxwell, Willelmus de Ramsay, Willelmus de Montealto, Alanus de Moravia, Donaldus Campbell, Joannes Cameron, Reginaldus le Chen, Alexander de Seton, Andreas de Lescelyne et Alexander de Straiton, ceterique barones et liberetenentes ac tota communitas regni Scotiae, omnimodam reverentiam filialem cum devotis pedum osculis beatorum.

Scimus, sanctissime Pater et Domine, et ex antiquorum gestis et libris colligimus, quod inter ceteras nationes egregias nostra scilicet Scotorum natio multis praeconiis fuerit insignita. Quae de majori Scythia per mare tyrrhenum et columnas Herculis transiens, et in Hispania inter ferocissimos per multa temporum curricula residens, a nullis quantumcumque barbaricis poterat alicubi subjugari, indeque veniens post mille et ducentos annos a transitu populi Israelitici sibi sedes in Occidente quas nunc obtinet, expulsis Britonibus et Pictis omnino deletis, licet per Norwegienses, Dacos et Anglicos saepius impugnata fuerit, multis sibi victoriis et laboribus quamplurimis acquisivit, ipsasque ab omni servitute liberas, ut priscorum testantur historiae, semper tenuit. In quorum regno centum et tredecim reges de ipsorum regali prosapia, nullo alienigena interveniente, regnaverunt.

Quorum nobilitates et merita, licet ex aliis non clarerent, satis patenter effulgent ex eo quod Rex regum et Dominus Jesus Christus post passionem et resurrectionem suam ipsos in ultimis terrae finibus constitutos quasi primos ad suam fidem sanctissimam convocavit, nec eos per quemlibet in dicta fide confirmari voluit sed per suum primum apostolum, quamvis ordine secundum vel tertium, scilicet Andream, mitissimum beati Petri germanum, quem semper ipsis praeesse voluit ut patronum.

Haec autem sanctissimi Patres et Praedecessores vestri, sollicita mente pensantes, ipsum regnum et populum ut beati Petri germani peculium multis favoribus et privilegiis quamplurimis munierunt. Ita quod gens nostra sub ipsorum protectione libera hactenus deguit et quieta, donec ille princeps magnificus Rex Anglorum Edwardus, pater istius qui nunc est, regnum nostrum acephalum populumque nullius mali aut doli conscium nec bellis aut insultibus tunc assuetum sub amici et confederati specie inamicabiliter infestavit.

Cuius injurias, caedes et violentias, praedationes, incendia, praelatorum incarcerationes, monasteriorum combustiones, religiosorum spoliationes et occisiones, alia quoque enormia quae in dicto populo exercuit, nulli parcens aetati aut sexui, religioni aut ordini, nullus scriberet nec ad plenum intelligeret nisi quem experientia informaret.

A quibus malis innumeris ipso juvante qui post vulnera medetur et sanat liberati sumus per strenuissimum Principem, Regem et Dominum nostrum, Dominum Robertum, qui pro populo et haereditate suis de manibus inimicorum liberandis quasi alter Maccabaeus aut Josue labores et taedia, inedias et pericula, laeto sustinuit animo.

Quem etiam divina dispositio et juxta leges et consuetudines nostras, quas usque ad mortem sustinere volumus, juris successio et debitus nostrorum omnium consensus et assensus nostrum fecerunt Principem atque Regem, cum tamquam illi per quem salus in populo facta est pro nostra libertate tuenda tam jure quam meritis tenemur et volumus in omnibus adhaerere.

Quem si ab inceptis desisteret, Regi Anglorum aut Anglicis nos aut Regem nostrum volens subjicere, tamquam inimicum nostrum et sui nostrique juris subversorem statim expellere niteremur et alium Regem nostrum, qui ad defensionem nostram sufficeret, faceremus.

Quia quamdiu centum vivi remanserint numquam Anglorum dominio aliquatenus volumus subjugari. Non enim propter gloriam, divitias aut honores pugnamus, sed propter libertatem solummodo, quam nemo bonus nisi simul cum vita amittit.

Hinc est, Reverende Pater et Domine, quod sanctitatem vestram omni precum instantia, genuflexis cordibus, exoramus, quatenus sincero corde menteque pia recensentes quod apud eum cuius vices in terris geritis non sit pondus in pondus nec distinctio Judaei et Graeci, Scoti aut Anglici, tribulationes et angustias nobis et Ecclesiae Dei illatas ab Anglicis paternis oculis intuentes Regem Anglorum, cui sufficere debet quod possidet, cum olim Anglia septem aut pluribus solebat sufficere Regibus, monere et exhortari dignemini ut nos Scotos in exili degentes Scotia, ultra quam habitatio non est, nihilque nisi nostrum cupientes, in pace dimittat. Cui pro nostra procuranda quiete quidquid possumus, ad statum nostrum respectu habito, facere volumus cum effectu.

Vestra enim interest, Sancte Pater, hoc facere, qui paganorum feritatem, Christianorum culpis exigentibus, in Christianos saevientem aspicitis et Christianorum terminos arctari in dies, quantumque vestrae sanctitatis memoriae derogat si, quod absit, Ecclesia in aliqua sua parte vestris temporibus patiatur eclipsim aut scandalum; vos videritis.

Excitet igitur Christianos Principes qui non causam ut causam ponentes se fingunt in subsidium terrae sanctae propter guerras quas habent cum proximis ire non posse. Cuius impedimenti causa est verior quod in minoribus proximis debellandis utilitas propior et resistentia debilior aestimantur. Sed quam laeto corde dictus dominus Rex noster et nos, si Rex Anglorum nos in pace dimitteret, illuc iremus, qui nihil ignorat satis novit. Quod Christi vicario totique Christianitati ostendimus et testamur.

Quibus si Sanctitas Vestra, Anglorum relatibus nimis credula, fidem sinceram non adhibet, aut ipsis in nostram confusionem favere non desinat, corporum excidia, animarum exitia, et cetera quae sequentur incommoda, quae ipsi in nobis et nos in ipsis fecerimus, vobis ab Altissimo credimus imputanda.

Ex quo sumus et erimus, in his quibus tenemur, tamquam obedientiae filii, vobis tamquam ipsius vicario in omnibus complacere, ipsique tamquam summo Regi et Judici causam nostram tuendam committimus, cogitatum nostrum jactantes in ipso sperantesque firmiter quod in nobis virtutem faciet et ad nihilum rediget hostes nostros.

Sanctitatem ac sanitatem vestram conservet Altissimus Ecclesiae suae sanctae per tempora diuturna.

Datum apud Monasterium de Aberbrothoc in Scotia, sexto die Aprilis, anno gratiae millesimo trecentesimo vicesimo, anno vero regni Regis nostri supradicti quinto decimo.

Postscript

by ANDY STEWART

As an adopted son of the town of Arbroath, I am delighted to add this postscript to James S. Adam's outstanding work in respect of the Declaration of the Scots. James Adam has admirably translated and transmitted both the sense and the passion of this letter and those who have read this will, I am sure, feel the same thrill that I did although I am ashamed to confess that I had to be content with the English and the Scots versions as my Gaelic is confined to the knowledge of a few songs in that great and noble language and my schoolboy-learned Latin is mainly long forgotten.

In August of 1951 and then again a year later I was lucky enough to be asked to take part in the Arbroath Abbey Pageant when the signing of the Declaration of Independence was re-enacted, splendidly, within the precincts of the ruined Abbey of Aberbrothock. In 1952, I spoke both the prologue and the epilogue to these "impressive scenes" as they were justifiably called by the Arbroath Herald. The epilogue summed up the whole spirit of the Pageant and incorporated the inspiring words of the ancient poet, John Barbour, on Freedom, a cry that came from the heart of a King who was the living soul of a nation.

I have never considered this occasion to be merely a theatrical experience, the whole Pageant had stirred its audience deeply in its simple and sincere re-enactment and the epilogue as I recited it from high atop a ruined plinth of the Abbey, seemed, like the Letter from Arbroath itself, to be in the right place at the right time. It was an experience that I shall never forget but remember with pride not in myself but in our noble ancestors who untiringly committed themselves to the freedom of our nation.

James Adam is a Dundonian with an Aberdonian, Buchan and Highland background. While still at school, he engaged in freelance journalism. He studied Accountancy and Company Secretaryship at the School of Accountancy in Glasgow. He took up newspaper work full-time via the advertisement department of the Scottish Daily Express. His advertising experience includes selling for the newspaper and three years as an account executive with an advertising agency. During the war, he trained as a wireless operator in the Royal Corps of Signals. He was commissioned into the General List as a Staff Officer working directly to the War Office.

After the war, he became successively Features Editor of the Glasgow Evening News, then of the Daily Record, then Assistant Editor of the Evening Times. He moved to Edinburgh on his appointment as Editor of the Weekly Scotsman, a paper which had world-wide readership among the scattered family of the Scot. He was given the task of devising and launching the Scottish TV Guide. He moved into newspaper management as General Manager of the Scotsman Publications. This was followed by appointments as Managing Director of the Chester Chronicle Newspapers and subsequently as Managing Director of the Middlesborough Evening Gazette.

A keen climber, camper and small boat enthusiast, he helped to pioneer the 1930s enthusiasm for the kayak, in which he made some adventurous journeys along the western seaboard and through the Inner and Outer Hebrides. Along with Sir Alastair Dunnett he travelled by kayak from the Clyde to Skye. The following year, he went by kayak from Skye to Scalpay, Harris, and then on to Stornoway, in the first solo crossing of the Minch by kayak. He has an unrivalled knowledge of Scotland and its people. His natal tongue is the vigorous Scots of the north-east. He taught himself some of the rudiments of Gaelic and attended the Advanced Gaelic conversation classes conducted by the Department of Extra-Mural Studies, Edinburgh University. He is a Past President of the Scottish Canoe Association, the Scottish Federation of Sea Anglers, past member of the Scottish Council of Physical Recreation and of the Cairngorm Winter Sports Development Board.

When he returned to Edinburgh in 1975, he was invited to organise the first ever International Gathering of the Clans which took place in 1977. In 1978/9 he was invited to represent Nova Scotia's first International Gathering of the Clans and to play a part in bringing Scots from the ends of the earth to Nova Scotia.

He was continually involved in the Scottish International Gathering Trust in the promotion of its imaginative objective which is to develop and extend international friendship based on that World-wide Family of the Scot. As a consequence, he enjoys close and lasting friendships spanning the continents.

Author, broadcaster and poet and in demand as a public speaker, he still makes time in a busy life for writing and particularly for the writing of verse in which he follows in the strong tradition of using Scots and Gaelic where appropriate.

He is a Fellow of the Institute of Directors and a Fellow of the Society of Antiquaries, Scotland.